ARTICULATED LOCOMOTIVES OF THE WORLD

ARTICULATED LOCOMOTIVES
OF THE WORLD

Donald Binns

D. BRADFORD BARTON LTD

**ARTICULATED LOCOMOTIVES
OF THE WORLD** a pictorial survey

Donald Binns

© *copyright D. Bradford Barton Ltd 1975*   *ISBN 0 85153 201 2*

printed in Great Britain by H. E. Warne Ltd, London and St. Austell

for the publishers

D. BRADFORD BARTON LTD · **Trethellan House** · **Truro** · **Cornwall** · **England**

contents

FRONTISPIECE:

South African Railways Class GMA Garratt No. 4134 near Worcester, Cape Province, March 1975. These big 4-8-2+2-8-4 Garratts are the most numerous class of articulated locomotives in the world and make an imposing sight. No. 4134, seen running bunker first and coupled to a tank car to supplement water capacity, was built by North British in 1958.

introduction

As far as can be traced, the articulated locomotive was invented in 1831 at the Neath Abbey Ironworks in South Wales, when drawings for a gear-driven articulated were produced for the Dowlais Iron Company and in all probability a locomotive was constructed to this design. On the other side of the Atlantic, Horatio Allen, who incidentally was one of the Neath Abbey Allens, designed a double boiler articulated 2-2-0+0-2-2, four being constructed for the South Carolina Railway in 1832. Little else occurred in the development of true articulated locomotives until 1850 when the Austrian Government announced the Semmering Locomotive Competition at which there appeared the progenitors of the Meyer and Fairlie forms of true articulated, along with one semi-articulated.

This book is a pictorial record of articulated locomotives, throughout the world, each of the main forms of true articulated being described briefly together with an accompanying series of photographs. One can touch only lightly on the technical details here and readers wishing to delve further into this fascinating subject are referred to *Articulated Locomotives* published originally in 1930 and reprinted in 1970. This standard reference work, by Prof. Lionel Wiener, sets out in great detail the numerous different forms of true and semi-articulated locomotives.

In this volume we are concerned only with the true articulated types, that is locomotives with two separate trucks capable of radial movement as on a bogie vehicle. Either one or both trucks can be driven from one, two, or more pairs of cylinders with the power transmitted by connecting rods, gearing, chains, etc.

Why were articulated locomotives needed? In many cases, overseas railways were built on a limited budget, resulting in the use of light track, foundations and bridges of insufficient strength. This type of railway was usually single track which restricted the number of trains workable. As these countries developed and trade prospered, longer and heavier trains became necessary but often this was impossible since conventional rigid-wheelbase locomotives could not be enlarged due to restricted axle loadings and severe curvature. The alternatives were to double-head longer trains—which was costly and uneconomical—or to re-lay lines to accept heavier motive power, this latter being expensive. So, locomotive engineers looked to articulation which was a cheap but effective answer to their problems, permitting large locomotives riding on two independent steam bogies which enabled them to negotiate sharp curves. Axle loadings could be kept within the limits due to the weight being spread over more axles whilst more powerful locomotives meant that heavier trains could be operated.

In other countries, articulated locomotives were necessary to haul heavy trains over difficult mountain sections where steep grades and sharp curves abounded. On sections such as these, conventional rigid frame locomotives were of little use and the operating departments found a satisfactory solution in the articulated.

Over the years many different forms of true articulated have been designed, built and tried—some satisfactorily, others quite the reverse. In the pages which follow, all the important and most of the lesser designs are illustrated and described.

ACKNOWLEDGEMENTS

The study of articulated locomotives generally has occupied me for the last 15 years during which time numerous letters have been written all over the world, often resulting in information and photographs. Several of the illustrations used in this book were acquired from correspondents who obtained prints from other sources and I would like to express my gratitude to all these as well as to the owners of photographs whose names I cannot now trace—without their help this book would not have been complete.

For permission to reproduce photographs I would especially like to thank: R. Abbott; A. H. Croxton; Guillermo Diaz; M. Feather; W. Holroyd; D. Ibbotson; M. Maïllet; R. S. McNaught; D. Trevor Rowe; J. Wiseman. Thanks are also due to: Antofagasta (Chile) & Bolivia Railway (London Office); D. Ferreira, Ravenglass & Eskdale Railway Company; South African Railways; Andrew Barclay Sons & Company Ltd; Hunslet Engine Company Ltd; Lokomotiv Fabrik Winterthur; Dresden Railway Museum; North West Museum of Science and Technology (for photographs from the Beyer Peacock Collection); Sheffield City Libraries (for use of photographs from the Yorkshire Engine Company Collection); Mitchell Library Collection (for use of photographs from the North British Locomotive Company Collection); the Alexander Turnbull Library of Wellington, New Zealand; the Swedish Railway Museum; Constable & Company (for permission to use certain illustrations from *Articulated Locomotives,* by L. Wiener (1930), and the 'Railway Magazine'.

Sincere thanks are also due to the staff of Skipton Public Library who have contributed greatly to my researches; also the National Lending Library for Science and Technology at Boston Spa, Yorkshire.

Skipton, Yorkshire   Donald Binns

THE SEMMERING COMPETITION OF 1851

A drawing of the Horatio Allen 2-2-0+0-2-2. Four of these locomotives were constructed in 1832 by the West Point Foundry for use on the South Carolina Railway, USA.

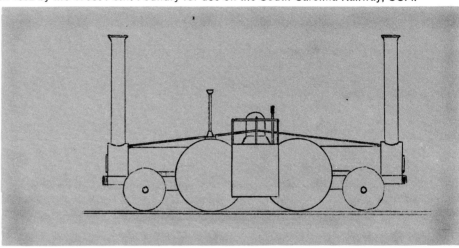

The Austrian Government originally authorised railway construction under a system of concessions granted to private companies. However, the southern line connecting Vienna with the seaport of Trieste was too much of a venture for private shareholders, involving as it did a crossing of the Alps at Semmering, so the Austrian Government decided to build the line themselves. Since the twelfth century the principal trade route connecting Vienna and the south was over the Semmering—the lowest of the Alpine passes, 3,040 ft. above sea level. The railway between Vienna and Wiener Neustadt had been opened by the Vienna-Raab Company during 1841 and extended in the following year to Gloggnitz on the northern face of the Semmering Pass. On 21 October 1844, the State-owned line from Murzzuschlag on the southern foot of the Semmering, opened to Graz, principal town of Styria and extended to Celje in 1846. In 1844 the route of the Semmering connecting section was finally agreed, the line opening during 1854. The Semmering Railway commenced at Gloggnitz and on the north side had 13¼ miles uphill at 1 in 40/46/47/54. From the summit 2,887 ft. above sea level, the line descended to Murzzuschlag at 1 in 50 for 8.3 miles. On the mountain section there were some 30 curves of 220 yds. radius, totalling about four miles, and a further 38 of 308 yds. radius.

By modern standards the Semmering is not difficult to operate but in the 1850s no suitable motive power existed and atmospheric power was considered but abandoned due to the expense. On rope haulage, Carlo de Ghega, engineer to the line, said, "the idea of using stationary engines and ropes was put out of the question by the sharpness of the curves and the great length of the line, which would have necessitated cumbrous machinery". An idea was formulated by the *Stuttgarter Eisenbahn Zeitung,* a technical magazine, to hold a locomotive competition and in May 1850 the Ministry of Commerce and Public Works announced that a locomotive competition would be held with a prize of 20,000 florins, the winning machine to become the property of the railway. The Government Locomotive Superintendent, Baron Engerth, said, "In the construction of a mountain line such as the Semmering, without any doubt, railways entered on a new phase, and consequently there was a necessity for new experiments upon locomotives also. There have certainly occurred on other lines short and steep gradients; but these have been so short not to necessitate any change in the locomotives from those used upon the level line. But a line of 21 miles in a region of snow and ice required something new which should be fit to cope with the peculiar difficulties of the situation.''

The requirements were worked out, including the tonnage to be hauled over the mountain section, fuel consumption, braking distance, boiler pressure, axle loading, etc. The competition took place on 31 July 1851, between Payerbach and Abfaltersbach, the distance being a little over 6 km, with many sharp curves, including one of 207 yds. radius. The ruling grade was 1 in 40, with an average of 1 in 54. The competition was judged by a committee comprising a railway director, a university professor, two independent mechanical engineers, Carlo de Ghega and two other railway engineers, one from Bavaria, the other from Hanover. This competition was important in articulated locomotive history, producing out of four entrants one semi-articulated and two true articulated designs, including the prototypes for the Meyer and Fairlie groups. These early locomotives were the progenitors of the more modern systems of articulation, forming the basis for later development.

The prize winner was an 0-4+4+6 semi-articulated locomotive built by J. A. Maffei of Hirscau, near Munich, named *Bavaria.* The leading two-axle truck was connected by side rods as was the second two-axle unit and the three-axle tender truck. Two cylinders at the front of the locomotive drove the first axle of the second truck and chains transmitted power from this axle to the rear axle of the front truck and from the rear axle of the second truck to the front axle

of the tender truck. As originally constructed, drive was taken to the rear axle of the second truck but before the competition this was altered to the front axle. In the competition *Bavaria* hauled a train of 132 tons up the 1 in 40 at 11.34 m.p.h., although the chain drive was not successful and numerous breakages occurred. With the chains out of commission, *Bavaria* was only equal to a four-coupled locomotive and was of little use on the Semmering. She never entered regular service and was dismantled soon after the competition.

Vindobona was a non-articulated 0-8-0 with the last axle behind the firebox and immediately beneath the footplate. A separate six-wheel tender was provided. Designed by John Haswell, Manager of the Staats Eisenbahn Gesellschaft (State Railway Company) workshops in Vienna, *Vindobona* was the first European 0-8-0. As originally conceived it was an 0-6-0 but on being weighed the axle loadings were found to be uneven and excessive, so Haswell introduced a fourth coupled axle. As an 0-8-0, the wheelbase was too long and Haswell then removed the rod coupling the first and second axles, making the locomotive into a 2-6-0. An interesting feature of the design was the counter pressure braking system invented by Haswell in conjunction with Johann Zeh, this preceding all the better known repression brake systems such as Le Chatelier, Riggenbach, etc. *Vindobona* had no brake blocks. On test it hauled 125 tons up the 1 in 40 at 6.87 m.p.h. Subsequently the locomotive was rebuilt by Haswell as an 0-6-4.

The prototype for the Fairlie group of true articulateds was *Seraing,* a double bogie 0-4+4-0T. Designed by Lausmann and built by the Société John Cockerill of Seraing in Belgium, it revived principles first employed in the American

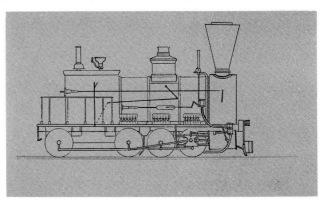

Semmering
competition locomotive
Vindobona; a
non-articulated 0-8-0 by
John Haswell of Vienna.
[Author's Collection]

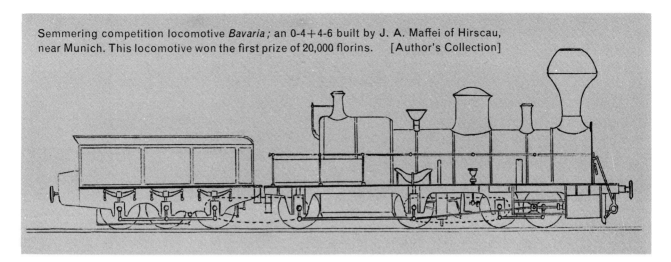

Semmering competition locomotive *Bavaria*; an 0-4+4-6 built by J. A. Maffei of Hirscau, near Munich. This locomotive won the first prize of 20,000 florins.   [Author's Collection]

Horatio Allen 2-2-0+0-2-2 of 1832. It had double boiler barrels with chimneys at the outer ends, the boilers resting on an inside main frame supported on circular castings and fixed pivots in sockets. A double firebox extended downwards between the two outside framed four-wheel steam bogies each driven from its own inside cylinders. The driving wheels on each bogie were connected by side rods. Buffing and drawgear was attached to the main frame. A centre cab was provided, the driver and fireman working at opposite sides of the firebox. Part of the fuel and water was carried on the locomotive, the rest in a separate tender attached to one end. A notable feature of the design was the power-assisted reversing gear, the servo-cylinder for which can be seen beneath the driver's footplate in the drawing. In the competition, *Seraing* hauled 126 tons up the 1 in 40 at 8.74 m.p.h. but could not make enough steam. Other problems lay in the steam connections and also in the inaccessibility of the motion.

The Meyer group of true articulateds was born at the Semmering competition in the shape of an 0-4+4-0T named *Wiener Neustadt*. This was the brain child of Wilhelm Gunther who constructed locomotives at Wiener Neustadt between 1842 and 1860, in which year his works amalgamated with G.Sigl to become Wiener Neustadt Lokomotivfabrik A.G. (Vormals G.Sigl). The *Wiener Neustadt* had a single boiler with rear fuel bunker, cab and side tanks carried on a main frame, the side pieces of which rested over the bogie frame sides in the normal position. This mainframe was

carried on two four-wheel steam bogies by circular seatings, a central pivot being provided for the front steam bogie. The wheels in each unit were coupled by side rods driven from a pair of cylinders located at the inner ends of each unit. Steam pipes were concentric with the bogies and had sliding joints with stuffing boxes. Buffing and drawgear was mounted on the main frame. In the competition this locomotive hauled 125 tons up the 1 in 40 at 6.87 m.p.h. but was not entirely successful due to insufficient flexibility of the steam bogies. No information appears to have survived regarding its subsequent disposal.

In September 1851, the Prize Committee awarded the 20,000 florins to the builders of *Bavaria* and also recommended the purchase of the other three locomotives, providing that in the case of the *Vindobona* alterations could be effected to the design. None of the four entered were entirely acceptable and Baron Engerth, then a departmental chief in the Ministry of Industry, rebuilt the *Bavaria* in 1852 by bringing the tender frames forward past the firebox, part of the weight of which they supported. The engine portion had one axle removed, becoming an 0-6-0 with two outside cylinders driving the third axle. The rear engine driving axle was connected to the front tender axle by gears and the tender wheels were coupled by rods on outside cranks. This Engerth design was patented and constructed for use in Austria, France, Switzerland and other European countries but being a semi-articulated is not part of this work and need not be further considered.

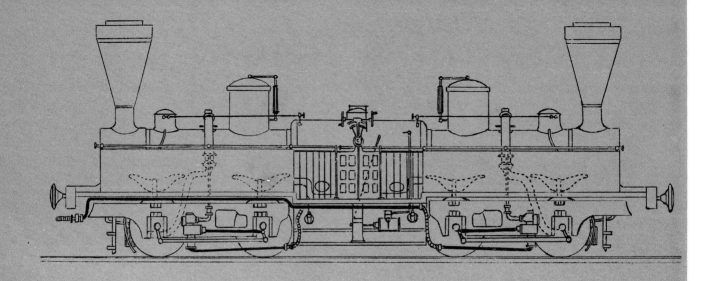

Semmering competition locomotive *Seraing*; prototype of the Fairlie group of articulateds. Designed by Lausmann and built by the Société John Cockerill of Seraing, Belgium.   [Author's Collection]

Semmering competition locomotive *Wiener Neustadt*; prototype of the Meyer group of articulateds. Designed by Wilhelm Gunther and built at Wiener Neustadt.   [Author's Collection]

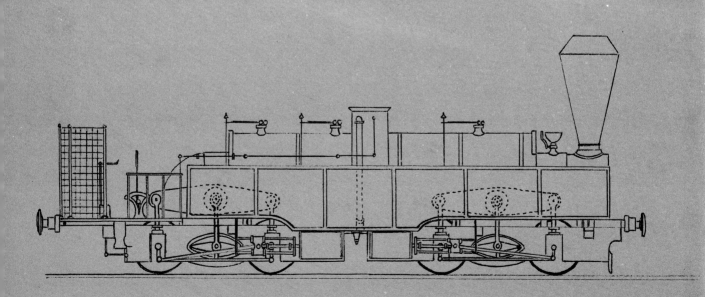

DOUBLE-BOILER FAIRLIE ARTICULATED

Robert Francis Fairlie was born in March 1831 and after receiving initial training at Crewe and Swindon he was appointed in 1853 engineer and general manager of the Londonderry & Coleraine Railway in Ireland. By the early 1860s, Fairlie had set up as a consulting engineer with offices at 56 Gracechurch Street, London, from which address he was engaged mainly on railway construction in India and South America. It was during this period that his articulated locomotive design was developed, the English patent being secured on 12 May 1864, covering "Improvements in Locomotive Engines and Boilers".

Fairlie's purpose in developing his articulated was to obtain a locomotive capable of producing a high tractive effort and yet free from the drawbacks associated with large rigid wheelbase machines. To overcome these problems, the Fairlie patent employed two steam bogies which allowed the locomotive to traverse curves impossible for large rigid wheelbase types. Like the *Seraing*, Fairlie's design used double boilers and central firebox so arranged as to make it unnecessary to turn the locomotive, it being equally suited to travelling in both directions. The driver and fireman worked at opposite sides of the central firebox but this arrangement was a disadvantage from the fireman's point of view as it restricted the space in which to swing his shovel properly. As Fairlie boilers became larger, the smaller became the working area and in some of the larger and more modern locomotives the problem was overcome by oil firing. Fuel was carried in bunkers along each side of the boilers or sometimes only on the fireman's side, whilst water was carried in side tanks. As with the *Seraing*, the small amount of fuel and water carried proved a disadvantage.

The boiler unit was supported on saddles at the smokebox ends and beneath these was a pivot which worked in bearings forming part of the steam bogie frames. The pivots were placed at dead centre position to each steam bogie wheelbase. On the *Seraing*, the pivots were attached to brackets but in the Fairlie design they were attached to the boiler shell. In 1869 this practice was discontinued and circular bogie centre castings were used. On *Seraing* the drawgear was mounted on the main frame carrying the double boilers but in the Fairlie the drawgear was mounted on the power bogies. Each steam bogie was a self-contained engine unit, having its own pair of cylinders driving two (or three) coupled axles, the cylinders being mounted outside the frames. At the outer ends of the boilers were smoke-boxes with chimneys mounted above in the normal manner but in his patent Fairlie noted a variation in which there were upper and lower series of boiler tubes. The lower passed from the firebox to the smokebox in the usual way whilst the upper led back to a smoke chamber placed over the central firebox and thence to a central chimney. A third series of tubes were also noted in the patent, to carry gases back from the central smoke chamber to smokeboxes at each outer end. This part of the patent was never applied, consequently no locomotives were constructed on this principle.

The Fairlie design was, of course, admirably suited to mountain railways requiring locomotives capable of negotiating sharp curves and climbing steep gradients. The design allowed steady riding over rough track although the Fairlie was essentially a low speed locomotive.

The first double boiler Fairlie was a 4 ft. 8½ in. gauge 0-4+4-0T named *Progress*, completed in December 1865, by James Cross & Company of St. Helens, for the Neath & Brecon Railway. The early Fairlies suffered from poor steam connection design and the single central firebox also proved unsatisfactory due to ineffective draughting. In an effort to overcome these problems, in September 1869, the first improved Fairlie entered service incorporating improved steam connections and at the same time with the central firebox divided in two, each having separate firedoors.

Between 1865 and 1911 single and double Fairlie locomotives were built by the following: James Cross & Company, of St. Helens; Fairlie Engine & Steam Carriage Company, of New Cross, London; The Avonside Engine Company Ltd, of Bristol; R & W Hawthorn & Company, of Newcastle on Tyne; the Hunslet Engine Company, of Leeds; Neilson & Company, of Glasgow; Sharp Stewart & Company, of Manchester; the North British Locomotive Company, of Glasgow; the Yorkshire Engine Company, of Sheffield; and Vulcan Foundry, of Newton-le-Willows. In Europe the type was constructed by Richard Hartmann of Chemnitz and G.Sigl of Wiener Neustadt. Several railway works also built Fairlie locomotives, including the Festiniog at Boston Lodge and the Kolomensky Works of the Russian State Railways. The type was used in England, Wales, Ireland, Canada, USA (Colorado), Mexico, South America, Cuba, South Africa, India, Burma, Norway, Sweden, France, Luxembourg, Saxony, Portugal, Russia, Australia and New Zealand.

Avonside Engine Company 0-6+6-0T Fairlie *Escaldor de Montes*; Works Number 958 of 1873. This locomotive belonged to the 3 ft. gauge Venezuelan Government Railways.
[Hunslet Engine Company]

Vulcan Foundry 0-4+4-0T Fairlie *Mountaineer*; Works Number 672 of 1873. Presented by the Duke of Sutherland to the 3 ft. gauge Denver & Rio Grande Railroad, this photograph was taken at the summit of the Veta Pass (altitude 4,700 ft.) on the line between Denver and Mexico City, via Santa Fé.
[Author's Collection]

The Fairlie Engine &
Steam Carriage
Company built this
0-4+4-0T Fairlie
Morton, in 1869. It was
delivered to a British
contractor (J. Morton &
Sons) and was
photographed on a
works train on the
Nassjo-Oscarshamn
Railway of Sweden.
  [Jarnvagsmuseum]

R. & W. Hawthorn &
Company 0-4+4-0T
Fairlie *Morlunda* (Works
Number 1638 of 1874)
on the Nassjo-
Oscarshamn Railway
in Sweden.
  [Jarnvagsmuseum]

A view dating
from the early
1870s of a
Fairlie on the
Wimmer Bridge,
Mexican
Railways.
[R. Abbott]

Yorkshire Engine Company 0-6+6-0T Fairlie, one of two built in 1891
(Works Numbers 446 and 447), for the 3 ft. 6 in. gauge Anglo-Chilian
Nitrate & Railway Company in South America.
[Yorkshire Engine Company Collection,
Sheffield City Library]

R. & W. Hawthorn & Company 0-4+4-0T Fairlie; Works Number 2013 of
1885. This locomotive was constructed for the 2 ft. 5½ in. gauge Saxon
State Railways and was eventually replaced by a Meyer type articulated.
[Verkehrsmuseum, Dresden]

17

Mexican Railways
Fairlie 0-6+6-0T
Papantla about 1890.
[R. Abbott]

Avonside Engine Company 0-4+4-0T Fairlie; Works Number 1245 of
1880 built for the metre gauge Indian State Railways.
[Hunslet Engine Company]

Yorkshire Engine Company 0-6+6-0T Fairlie, one of three built in 1883
(Works Numbers 365-367), for the Mexican Railways.
[Yorkshire Engine Company Collection,
Sheffield City Library]

Avonside Engine Company 0-6+6-0T
Fairlie; Works Number 887 of 1872 for
the 4 ft. 8½ in. gauge Nitrate Railways
of Chile.   [Author's Collection]

Neilson & Company Fairlie *Tecolutla* of
the Mexican Railways.   [R. Abbott]

VULCAN FOUNDRY MODIFIED FAIRLIE

In 1901 Vulcan Foundry produced a modified design of double-boiler Fairlie locomotive incorporating separate boilers and fireboxes carried on a deep girder frame. In this type, a walk-through cab was provided, this being far safer for the enginemen who, on the earlier Fairlies, were liable to be crushed if the locomotive overturned. The modified locomotives were of course rather longer than the conventional Fairlie, the increased length being that of the walk-through cab between the fireboxes. At the same time the steam piping was improved by reducing the number of connections and the point of pivot was also altered, the smokebox end of the boiler being mounted on castings fixed to the far outer ends of the frames and the underside of these castings formed the pivots for the bogies. A matching casting fixed between the bogie frames formed a socket for the pivot. On the conventional Fairlie, it will be recalled, the point of pivot was the dead centre of the bogie wheelbase whereas on the Vulcan modification the pivot was advanced to the smokebox end. This type was used only on the Burma Railway and on the Junin Railway in Chile.

Yorkshire Engine Company 0-6+6-0T Modified Fairlie, *San Antonio* (Works Number 834 of 1905) with two separate fireboxes and walk-through cab; built for the 2 ft. 6 in. gauge Junin Railway in Chile.
[Yorkshire Engine Company Collection, Sheffield City Library]

FAIRLIE - MALLET ARTICULATEDS

Three locomotives based on this hybrid principle were built for metre gauge industrial branches on the Saxon State Railways where there were curves of 98 ft. radius. Anatole Mallet suggested the addition of compounding to the Fairlie principle, hence the name Fairlie Mallet—or Fairlie Lindner as they were sometimes known. These locomotives were built at the Sachsische Maschinenfabrikvorm Richard Hartmann of Chemnitz, and were of the 0-4+4-0T type. The cylinders were at the inner ends of each steam bogie, so reducing the distance of steam passage between high and low pressure cylinders. These Chemnitz Fairlies were also unusual in that steam and brake controls were mounted at each end of the locomotive in addition to those in the centre cab, an arrangement made necessary owing to a certain amount of running over public roads. To enable the driver to walk from one end of the locomotive to the other, a full length canopy with side panels was provided. The Heusinger valve gear was also enclosed by side plates reminiscent of a tram engine. Later the canopy was removed and the driver operated only the centre cab. These compound Fairlies were eventually replaced by Meyer articulateds which had a conventional and more convenient driving position.

Richard Hartmann compound Fairlie 0-4+4-0T; this class of three former Saxon State Railways locomotives were renumbered 99.161 to 99.163 by Deutsche Reichsbahn in the 1920s and No. 99.161 is photographed with its canopy removed.
[Verkehrsmuseum, Dresden]

Richard Hartmann, of the Saxon Engine Works, Chemnitz, built this 0-4+4-0T compound Fairlie in 1902 for the metre gauge Saxon State Railways. This photograph shows the locomotive in original condition.
[Verkehrsmuseum, Dresden]

Compound Fairlie No.99.162 hauling a standard gauge wagon on metre gauge transporter bogies.
[Verkehrsmuseum, Dresden]

PECHOT BOURDON ARTICULATEDS

Another design similar to that of Robert Fairlie was the French Pechot Bourdon locomotive patented in June 1837 by two artillery officers, Messrs. Pechot and Bourdon. The first Pechot Bourdon was a small double-boiler articulated weighing 12 tons 2 cwt. in working order and measuring 18 ft. 11 in. long, 4 ft. 6 in. overall width and 9 ft. 10 in. high. It was capable of doing the work of two ordinary rigid frame 0-4-0 tanks and at the same time could run over light track and negotiate sharp curves. The design was practically the same as the original Fairlie in which the boilers, central firebox and cab were mounted on a frame carried by two four-wheel steam bogies with cylinders placed at the outer ends. Unlike the later Fairlies, the Pechot Bourdon had one firebox for both boilers and there was no central dividing plate. A single steam dome was mounted above the firebox and the design incorporated simplified steam piping and spring compensation between the boiler and the rear of the steam bogies, the purpose of this being to equalise the load on the axles. The drawgear was attached at a point near to the bogie centres.

One of these locomotives, constructed by the Anciens Etablissements Cail, of Denain, was shown at the 1889 Paris Exhibition. Prior to the First World War, the French used 60 cm. gauge railways extensively to serve their military establishments and during the 1914-18 war the type was adopted by the French Military Railways and constructed in large numbers, being used in moving heavy armaments such as long range guns. For other than military purposes, however, there has been little application of the Pechot Bourdon design.

Pechot Bourdon 0-4+4-0T No. 215 being delivered to the Railway Museum at Dresden.
[Verkehrsmuseum, Dresden]

▶
The same locomotive in position in the museum at Dresden.
[Verkehrsmuseum, Dresden]

25

A head-on view of the preserved Pechot Bourdon 0-4+4-0T.
[Verkehrsmuseum, Dresden]

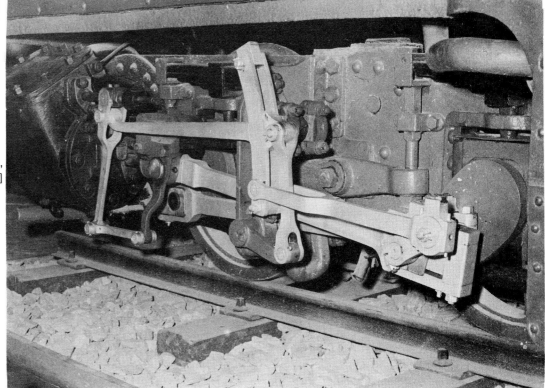

Cylinders and valve gear of the Pechot Bourdon locomotive.
[Verkehrsmuseum, Dresden]

Cab and controls of the same Pechot Bourdon locomotive. [Verkehrsmuseum, Dresden]

A large double-boiler true articulated was designed by Charles Thouvenot, of Bex, and patented in France on 20 August 1863. This was intended for hauling heavy trains through the Alps and had two steam bogies each with three coupled axles. Each centrally pivoted bogie had its own pair of outside cylinders mounted on the inner ends of the units. The double boiler with central firebox was mounted on a main frame supported on the bogie frame by lateral rollers. Water was carried in tanks below the boiler.

A development of the Thouvenot system occurred in 1867 when G. T. Lommell, of St. Gall in Switzerland, completed designs for an articulated locomotive on the same principle but modified to allow it to work over rack railways laid on the Fell system. This was intended for use on the proposed Trans-Alpine Lukmanier Railway.

Large 0-6+6-0T articulated locomotive designed by Charles Thouvenot and intended for working heavy trains through the Alps.   [Author's Collection]

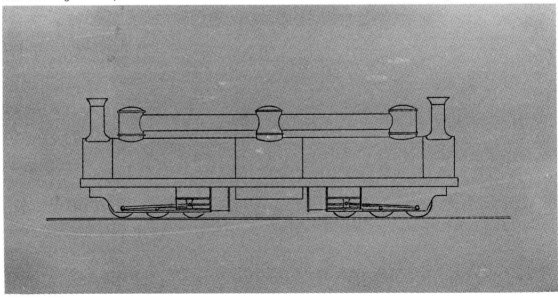

SINGLE-BOILER FAIRLIE ARTICULATEDS

All the Fairlie locomotives so far illustrated had double boilers and independent steam bogies, but neither of these features was essential to the system of articulation and Fairlie built a number of single-boiler locomotives with one set of cylinders, one power and one non-power bogie. These single-boiler machines with one steam bogie were still true articulateds since both sets of wheels were capable of sideways movement and could take up any position independent of each other and of the boiler.

The first, an 0-4-4T, was built in 1869 at the Inchicore works of the Great Southern & Western Railway of Ireland. The largest user was the New Zealand Government Railways who took delivery of eighteen 0-6-4Ts from the Avonside Engine Company in 1878-9 and a further seven similar locomotives in 1880-1. In Wales the single Fairlie was used on both the North Wales Narrow Gauge Railway and on the Festiniog. In total, few were constructed and they were found only in England, Wales, Ireland, Australia and New Zealand.

R. & W. Hawthorn & Company 0-4-4T single boiler Fairlie (Works number 1699 of 1877) built for the Swindon, Marlborough & Andover Railway.   [Author's Collection]

29

Hunslet Engine Company 0-6-4T single boiler Fairlie; Works Number
979 of 1908, built for the North Wales Narrow Gauge Railway.

[Hunslet Engine Company]

FAIRLIE LOCOMOTIVES IN THE USA

In 1869 an American, William Mason of the Mason Machine Works of Taunton in Massachusetts, produced designs for an 0-6+6-0T similar to the double-boiler Fairlie. Built in 1871, the *Janus* was tried out on the Boston & Albany Railroad before going to the Central Pacific in California from where it was eventually sold to the Lehigh Valley Railroad, Pennsylvania, spending part of its short life on pusher service on Wilkes-Barre mountain. *Janus* proved unsatisfactory and Mason constructed no further double-boiler Fairlies, this solitary example finally being converted to make two 0-6-0 shunters.

Mason then turned his attentions to the single-boiler Fairlie type which in the United States became known as Mason-Fairlie, or Mason Bogies. The first appeared in 1871, being sold in July 1872 to the American Fork Railroad. This was a 3 ft. gauge 0-4-4T named *Onward*. Mason Bogies were

constructed in a wide variety of wheel arrangements: 0-4-4, 0-4-6, 2-4-4, 2-4-6, 0-6-4, 0-6-6, 2-6-6 and 2-8-6. The largest users were the Boston, Revere Beach & Lynn, Denver South Park & Pacific, New York & Manhattan Beach and the Wheeling & Lake Erie railroads. The great majority were employed within the United States but two were exported to Cuba, two to Mexico, four to Canada and a further three worked in New Brunswick.

Mason did not enjoy a great deal of success as a locomotive builder and ceased construction in 1890; in fact his last Fairlie type had been delivered in 1887. Then, the Manchester Locomotive Works, in New Hampshire (later forming part of ALCO) took over the construction of Mason-Fairlies. ALCO continued to fill orders until 1914 when the last one emerged from the Schenectady plant for the 3 ft. gauge Boston, Revere Beach & Lynn Railroad.

Mason Machine Works, Taunton (Massachusetts) 0-6+6-0T Fairlie *Janus ;* Works Number 438 of 1871. This was the only double boiler Fairlie constructed in the USA.   [R. Abbott]

31

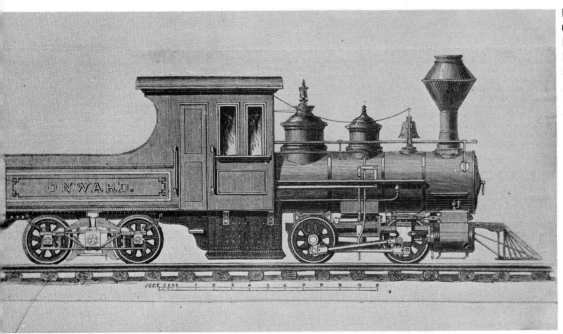

Mason Machine Works 0-4-4T single boiler Fairlie *Onward*, Works Number 461 of 1871. Sold to the 3 ft. gauge American Fork Railroad in Utah, this was the first Mason-Fairlie to be built.

[R. Abbott]

Mason Machine Works 0-6-6T single boiler Fairlie; Works Number 536 of 1874. Constructed for the 3 ft. gauge New Bedford Railway in Massachusetts, this was the first locomotive in the USA to have Walschaerts valve gear.   [R. Abbott]

Hoosac Tunnel &
Wilmington Railroad
(USA) locomotive No.
3—a single boiler
Fairlie 0-4-4T.
[R. Abbott]

Mason Machine Works
2-4-4T single boiler
Fairlie *Matthew
Craddock;* Works
Number 746 of 1887.
This locomotive
became No. 100 of the
4 ft. 8½ in. gauge
Boston & Maine
Railroad.   [R. Abbott]

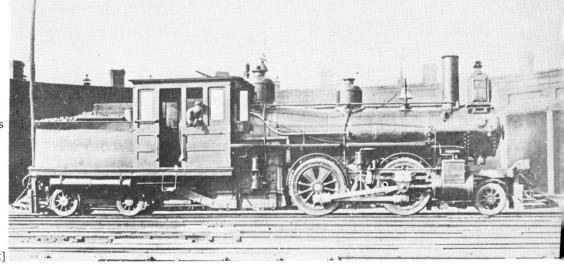

JOHNSTONE ARTICULATED LOCOMOTIVES

In the United States, Johnstone produced a design for a compound 2-6+6-2T for the 4 ft. 8½ in. gauge Mexican Central Railway. Three locomotives were built in 1885 by the Rhode Island Locomotive Works of Providence (later part of ALCO), and these had two boilers and two fireboxes but unlike a Fairlie had cylinders which were attached to the main frame and not to the bogies, motion being transmitted through a curious and complex system of rods. This system and the fact that they were compounds made them expensive to maintain and lacking in reliability and after a few years they were replaced.

Johnstone then produced a somewhat similar design but this time incorporating two separate boilers and walk-through cab. Again built by the Rhode Island Locomotive Works, a number were constructed in 1888 for the Mexican Central Railway. Whilst being delivered to Mexico these locomotives were found to be so large as to make it neces-

sary to dismantle them partially for transit through the Raton Pass tunnel. They were of the compound type with concentric pistons, the inner being the high pressure and the outer the low pressure, driving the wheels through the rod system.

In 1886 Johnstone produced an interesting design for a single boiler locomotive in which the boiler, cab and tender were mounted on a continuous frame. This was supported by two 4-6-0 steam bogies, each driven by a pair of cylinders mounted above the leading four-wheel bogies, but again fixed to the main frames. These were also intended for the Mexican Central but it is doubtful if any actual locomotives were constructed to this design. Yet another design prepared by Johnstone was similar to this 4-6-0+4-6-0 but employed two four-wheel non-powered bogies under the tender portion instead of the 4-6-0 steam bogie.

Johnstone 2-6+6-2T of 1885 for the 4 ft. 8½ in. gauge Mexican Central Railway.   [Constable & Company]

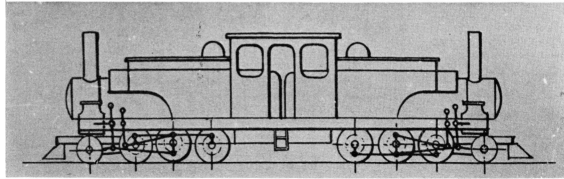

34

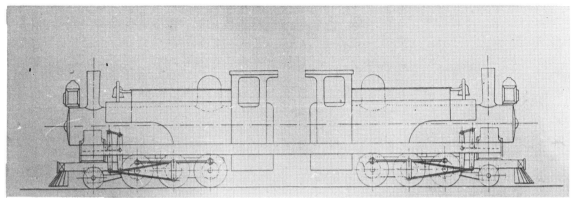

Johnstone 2-6+6-2T of 1888 for the Mexican Central Railway.   [Constable & Company]

Johnstone 4-6-0+4-6-0 designed, but probably not built. Intended for the Mexican Central Railway.   [Author's Collection]

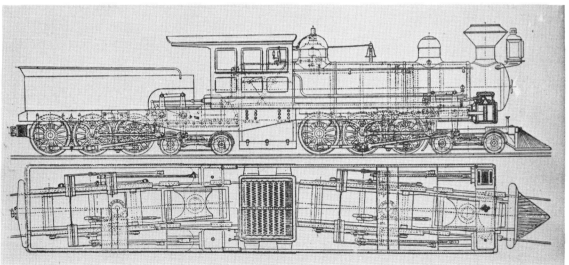

GOLWE ARTICULATED LOCOMOTIVE

The Golwé articulated locomotive was patented in 1924 and was the brain child of G. Goldschmidt and A. Weber, managing director and chief engineer respectively of the Société Haine St. Pierre in Belgium. In this design the boiler, cab, rear water tank and fuel bunker were mounted on a plate girder frame resting on two independent steam bogies. Pivots were positioned mid-way between the outermost axles of each bogie. The main frame was carried by centre pivots on both bogies, those supporting the boiler being hemi-spherical steel castings while corresponding concave bogie pivots lined with phosphor-bronze formed oil reser-

voirs for lubrication. Lateral swing between upper and lower parts when rounding curves was counteracted by springs. The design allowed for a deep firebox slung between the steam bogies.

Four Golwé 2-6-0+0-6-2 locomotives were built by the Société Haine St. Pierre in 1928 to the order of the Minister of French Colonies for the Chemin de Fer de la Côte d'Ivoire in French West Africa. As far as can be traced no other Golwé type articulateds were constructed, the design not being further exploited due mainly to a preference for the Beyer Garratt.

Drawing of the Golwé 2-6+6-2T built by the Société Haine St. Pierre in 1928 to the order of the Minister of French Colonies for the Chemin de fer de la Côte d'Ivoire.   [Author's Collection]

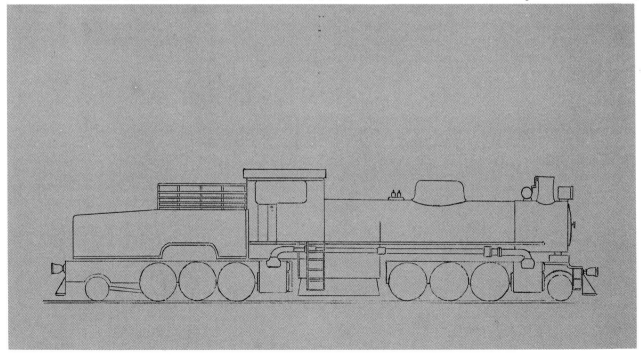

MEYER ARTICULATEDS

On 15 March 1861, Jean Jacques Meyer and his son Adolphe were granted a French patent for "a system of complete articulation for tank engines". In the following year, Meyer exhibited various designs at the International Machinery Exhibition held at South Kensington. One of these was for "an articulated tank locomotive of great power", an 0-6+6-0T coupled by side rods, the design being a development of the *Wiener Neustadt* entered in the 1851 Semmering competition. Each independent steam bogie was driven from its own pair of cylinders mounted on the inner ends, and buffing and drawgear was affixed to the steam bogies which were connected by a tie bar which clasped the pivot castings—in this way no buffing or traction stresses were transmitted to the boiler or its supports. The boiler was carried on the front steam bogie, the water tank being placed at the front of the locomotive and the coal boxes behind the cab. The boiler was supported on the front steam bogie by a spherical pivot at the centre over the middle axle, which worked in a socket attached to the underside of the boiler barrel. There were two supports on the rear unit which carried part of the superstructure by brackets on the frames supporting semi-spherical bearings on sliding plates at either side of the back end of the firebox. Meyer calculated the tractive effort at 22,000 lbs; enough to take a train weighing (inclusive of the locomotive) 2,300 tons on level track at 10 m.p.h., or 340 tons up 1 in 40 and 155 tons up 1 in 17 at 10 m.p.h.

The first Meyer articulated tank locomotive, a 4 ft. 8½ in. gauge 0-4+4-0 named *L'Avenir*—not to be confused with one of the same name built some years later on the Mallet system—was constructed with the help of a state subsidy in 1868 by Parent Schacken, Compagnie de Fives Lille, for M. Meyer of Mulhouse. After trials in France, Belgium and Switzerland it was eventually returned to the Chemin de fer des Charentes in France. A further application of the Meyer principle took place in 1873 when the Anciens Etablissements Cail, of Denain, constructed two large 0-6+6-0T for the Chemin de fer de l'Herault in France. Both were successful and remained in service until 1907.

The Meyer principle was further developed by Charles Evrard, director of the Compagnie Belge of Brussels, who in 1873 built an 0-6+6-0T Meyer which was shown at the Vienna Exhibition before being sent to the Chemin de fer du Grand Central Belge for use on the line to Lodelinsart.

Several other simple expansion Meyer locomotives were built by Continental makers over the years and the type was also constructed by three British builders. Andrew Barclay Sons & Company built four different narrow gauge Meyer locomotives between 1903 and 1928. W. G. Bagnall Ltd of Stafford built a narrow gauge Meyer about 1936 on which the cylinders were mounted on the inner ends of each steam bogie. The boiler, side tanks, cab and bunker were carried on a rigid upper frame, this being connected to the bogie units through cast steel bogie centres. The design was revived in 1953 when two locomotives were built for a 2 ft gauge sugar estate railway in Natal, the design being favoured because of its compactness in comparison to a Beyer Garratt of similar power. A third locomotive was supplied to Bowaters Lloyd Paper Mills at Sittingbourne in Kent; this was sold in 1966 to the Welshpool & Llanfair Light Railway, where it is now preserved.

Two extremely powerful 0-6+6-0T Meyer locomotives were built by the Yorkshire Engine Company in 1912 for the El Ferrocarril Salitrero (Nitrate Railways of Chile). From Iquique (26 ft. above sea-level) the FCS ran almost level for 2½ miles before commencing a difficult climb along the mountainside to a point 3,000 ft. above sea level, reached in 19¼ miles at Las Carpas. The average grade was 1 in 35, varying between 1 in 40 and 1 in 25 with sections as steep as 1 in 22. No less than 173 curves existed on this section, some as sharp as 300 ft. radius and many were separated by almost negligible straights. Over this section the Meyer locomotives hauled 208 ton trains at just over 8 m.p.h. without any stop for water.

Beyer Peacock & Company Ltd of Manchester also constructed six unusual Meyer 0-6-2+0-6-2s for the Antofagasta (Chile) & Bolivia Railway, details of which are included in the section devoted to Kitson Meyer locomotives.

Simple expansion Meyers were built in small numbers and were confined principally to Europe, including England, Belgium, France, Switzerland, Denmark, Sweden and possibly Portugal. Outside Europe, isolated examples have been used in India, Natal, the Straits Settlements, Tasmania, Greece, Chile and Bolivia.

Design for an articulated tank locomotive by J. J. and A. Meyer of Vienna, displayed at the International Machinery Exhibition, London, in 1862.
[Author's Collection]

A further design by J. J. and A. Meyer, also displayed at the International Machinery Exhibition.
[Author's Collection]

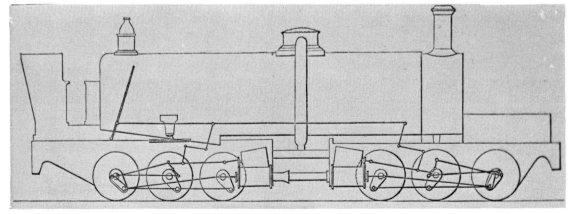

Meyer 0-6+6-0T built by the Anciens Etablissements Cail of Denain, France, in 1873. This locomotive became No. 151 of the Chemin de fer de l'Herault.   [M. Maillet]

Meyer 0-6+6-0T built by the Compagnie Belge, of Brussels, in 1873. This locomotive was displayed at the Vienna Exhibition before being delivered to the Chemin de fer du Grand Central Belge.   [Constable & Company]

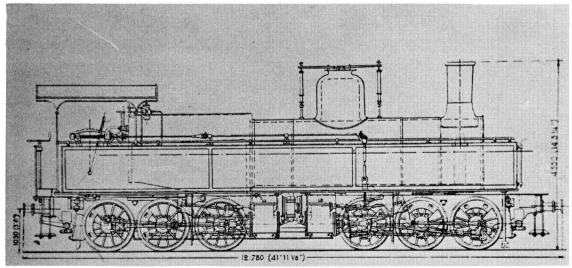

Andrew Barclay Sons & Company 0-6+6-0T Meyer *High Ranger;* Works Number 1369 of 1914. This locomotive was delivered to the 2 ft. gauge railway of J. Finlay & Company Ltd., Calcutta, and was probably used to haul logs.   [Andrew Barclay Sons & Co.]

This handsome little Meyer 0-4+4-0T, built by Andrew Barclay Sons & Company in 1903 (Works Number 960) was for the 2 ft. 5½ in. gauge Anglo-Greek Magnesite Company.

[Andrew Barclay Sons & Company]

Yorkshire Engine Company 0-6+6-0T Meyer. One of two locomotives
built in 1912 (Works Numbers 940/1), for the 4 ft. 8½ in. gauge Nitrate
Railways of Chile.　　　　　　　　[Yorkshire Engine Company Collection,
Sheffield City Library]

MEYER ARTICULATED COMPOUNDS

Meyer compound tank locomotives have been constructed to both 2 ft. 5$\frac{1}{2}$ in. and 4 ft. 8$\frac{1}{2}$ in. gauges for the Saxon State Railways, part of whose system traversed mountainous areas necessitating sharp curvature and steep grades. They had tried various different forms of articulation including Klose, Klien-Lindner, Fairlie Compound, Mallet and the weird and wonderful Hagans 0-6-4T. Richard Hartmann built the first narrow gauge Meyer locomotives of Class 1 VK and between 1892 and 1921 delivered 96 of these. The boiler, cab, side tanks and fuel bunker were laid out in conventional manner, the superstructure being carried on two four-wheel steam bogies each driven from its own pair of cylinders mounted on the inner ends of each unit. Two low pressure cylinders were carried on the front unit, high pressure on the rear. The steam bogies were connected by an obliquely mounted coupling bar from the left side of the rear of the leading unit to the right side of the front of the trailing one. In service these Meyer compounds could haul 150 ton trains at 9.3 m.p.h. up 1 in 40 gradients with long curves of 218 ft. radius. In recent years many have been given new boilers and frames and some are still in service. Narrow gauge compound Meyers were also used on the 60 cm. gauge Osnabruck Railway whilst standard gauge ones were in use on the 4 ft. 8$\frac{1}{2}$ in. gauge lines elsewhere on the Saxon State Railways. These were also constructed by Richard Hartmann and could haul 195 tons at 15$\frac{1}{2}$ m.p.h. up 1 in 25 grades. The last of them was withdrawn from service during 1967 and one is preserved at the Verkehrsmuseum in Dresden.

Richard Hartmann
0-4+4-0T Meyer.
Former Saxon State
Railways 2 ft. 5$\frac{1}{2}$ in.
gauge, now DDR
99.1566.1 at Oschatz,
on the Oschatz-Mügeln
line, 1974.

[M. Feather]

An ex-German
0-4+4-0T Meyer at
Tirgu Mures in
Roumania.
[W. Holroyd]

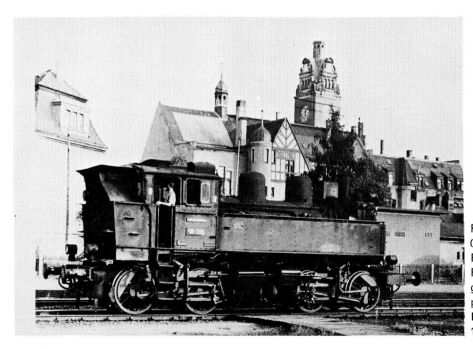

Richard Hartmann
0-4+4-0T Meyer.
Former Saxon State
Railways 4 ft. 8½ in.
gauge, now DR 98.015
photographed at
Dresden in August
1963. [D. Trevor Rowe]

44

MEYER ARTICULATED SNOWPLOUGH

A variation based on the Meyer system of articulation appeared in a special purpose metre gauge 0-6+6-0 rotary snowplough built in 1910 by the Lokomotiv Fabrik Winterthur for the Chemin de fer de la Bernina in Switzerland.

The Bernina electric railway connected Tirano, 1,407 ft. above sea level, with St. Moritz at 5,833 ft., by way of the Bernina Pass and Pontresina. *En route* it reached the highest altitude of any adhesion-worked European railway, at Bernina Hospice station at 7,400 ft. elevation. As might be expected, the line was liable to heavy snowfall, often resulting in partial closure. Experience proved that small rotary ploughs pushed by electric motor cars were not satisfactory and it was considered that electric locomotives would be little better, since at that date it was impossible to supply sufficient electrical output from overhead wires to drive the unit—the rotor blades requiring 500-600 horse power and the locomotive itself a further 300-400. The Bernina line had 1 in 14 adhesion grades with 148 ft. radius curves and the Meyer form of articulation seemed an excellent basis on which to produce a self-powered rotary snow plough.

The superstructure was carried on two six-wheel steam bogies with four simple admission cylinders mounted on the inner ends of each unit. The superstructure frame also carried the snow clearing mechanism, the rotary cleaner being driven by a separate engine with cylinders mounted on each side above running plate level, between the locomotive cylinders. In service, the Meyer had a four-wheel tender and the whole unit was covered by a wood sheathing.

Special purpose Meyer rotary snowplough locomotive constructed by the Lokomotiv Fabrik Winterthur for the metre gauge Swiss Bernina Railway. This photograph shows the unit with wood sheathing removed.

[Lokomotiv Fabrik Winterthur]

The cylinders and motion of the Meyer rotary snowplough locomotive of the Bernina Railway. The cylinders mounted above footplate level drove the plough rotors.

[Lokomotiv Fabrik Winterthur]

The Meyer snowplough in action on the Bernina line.   [Lokomotiv Fabrik Winterthur]

47

MODIFIED COMPOUND MEYER

In 1892 one, or possibly two, 0-6+6-0T locomotives were built by the Baldwin Locomotive Works for the Sinnemahoning Valley Railroad—a logging line in western Pennsylvania. These were on the Meyer principle but differed from early Meyers in that the boiler, cab, side tanks and rear fuel bunker were carried on a girder frame to which link and pin couplers were attached, the whole resting on two six wheel steam bogies. Vauclain compounding was employed, the cylinders being mounted at the rear of each bogie. It was from this modified Meyer that Robert Stirling developed the Kitson Meyer articulated.

Baldwin Locomotive Works 0-6+6-0T modified Meyer compound built in 1892. This locomotive became No. 3 of the Sinnemahoning Valley Railroad in western Pennsylvania.   [Author's Collection]

Robert Stephenson Ltd 2-8+8-2T Kitson Meyer, one of two built for Kitson & Company by Robert Stephenson and carrying Kitson Works Numbers 5471 and 5472 of 1935. These locomotives were for the 3 ft. gauge Girardot Railway in Colombia and were the last Kitson Meyer type constructed. They were withdrawn from service in 1958.
[Guillermo Diaz, per Trevor Rowe]

KITSON MEYER ARTICULATEDS

The prototype Kitson Meyer was constructed for the 3 ft. 6 in. gauge Ferrocarril Tocopilla al Toco (Anglo-Chilian Nitrate & Railway Company) in 1894 and the type owes much to Robert Stirling, Locomotive Superintendent of that road. For the opening, Kitson & Company of Leeds had supplied a rigid 4-8-4T but, due to an increase in nitrate traffic, larger motive power was soon needed so Stirling designed an articulated locomotive on the Meyer principle. In 1892 the Balwin Locomotive Works had built the modified 0-6+6-0T compound Meyer and it seems almost certain that Robert Stirling must have examined this either under construction or in service since his new design was more than similar. The reason for Stirling's articulated was of course the FTT's need for a locomotive capable of working heavy trains over 17 miles of continuous 1 in 24, much of which was combined with 181 ft. radius curves. Although Kitson & Company gave little credit, Robert Stirling played an important part in the development of the Kitson Meyer design and without him it would probably never have come into being.

The prototype had two six-wheel steam bogies (0-6+6-0T), each driven from its own pair of cylinders mounted at the rear of the units. The boiler, cab, fuel and water supplies were laid out in conventional manner on a girder frame supported on the steam bogies. Pivots were built into the superstructure, working in sockets integral with the steam bogies. In early Kitson Meyer designs, exhaust from the rear steam bogie was carried through piping in the water tanks, slightly pre-heating the feed water before passing into a rear chimney behind the cab. In later designs, rear steam bogie exhaust returned to the smokebox where it was exhausted in the usual way. The design produced a compact locomotive with only the firebox between the steam bogies.

The Kitson Meyer design passed through various stages of development and the principal types are as follows:

1. Simple tank locomotives with the cylinders at the rear of each bogie: 0-6+6-0T.

2. Simple locomotives with the cylinders at the rear of each bogie and with separate tenders: 0-6+6-0, 0-6-2+0-6-2 (these latter built by Beyer Peacock).

3. Simple tank locomotives with the cylinders at the outer ends of each bogie: 0-6+6-0T, 2-6+6-2T, 2-6-2+2-6-2T, 2-8+8-0T and 2-8+8-2T. These were a development of the earlier locomotives. In this type the steam bogies were usually placed further apart and the use of leading and/or trailing trucks extended to most designs. Water capacity was increased, with the side tanks usually divided leaving the firebox area clear for easy access to the centre of the locomotive. One part of the tank was located behind the cab and the other hung pannier fashion over the front portion of the boiler.

4. Simple tank locomotives with the cylinders at the outer ends of each bogie. This type had three bogies of which only two were driven: 2-6+6-4T.

5. Combined rack and adhesion 0-8+6-0T for the Argentine and Chilian Transandine Railways only.

The Kitson Meyer was South America's special articulated, being employed on several lines where operating conditions were amongst the most arduous in the world. The type was employed in other parts of the world also but found greatest favour on the South American roads which climbed the Andes, notably in Chile, Bolivia and Colombia.

Kitson & Company 0-6+6-0T Kitson Meyer locomotive with cylinders at the rear of each unit and with separate tender. This photograph of Rhodesian Railways No. 52 was taken at Wankie in 1907.

[A. H. Croxton]

An early photograph on the Taltal Railway in Chile, showing a Kitson Meyer 0-6+6-0T shunting wagons of sacked nitrate into storage sheds at Taltal. [Railway Magazine]

3 ft. 6 in. gauge Kitson Meyer 0-6+6-0T No. 50 moving No. 61 from the workshops to the running shed at Taltal in 1971. [J. Wiseman]

One of two Kitson & Company 2-6+6-2T Kitson Meyers built in 1928 (Works Numbers 5416 and 5417), for the 3 ft. gauge Cundinamarca Railway, in Colombia.

[Guillermo Diaz, per Trevor Rowe]

Kitson & Company 2-6+6-2T Kitson Meyer. One of four supplied in 1927; Works Numbers 5400-5403, to the 3 ft. gauge Girardot Railway of Colombia. A similar locomotive was supplied during 1929 to the Cundinamarca Railway; Works Number 5431.

[Guillermo Diaz, per Trevor Rowe]

Beyer Peacock & Company Ltd 0-6-2+0-6-2 Kitson Meyer type locomotive. This series of six were intended for running cab-forward over the Antofagasta (Chile) & Bolivia Railway and, as constructed, were coal fired.
[North Western Museum of Science and Industry]

Beyer Peacock & Company Ltd 0-6-2+0-6-2 Kitson Meyer locomotive of the same class as that illustrated above, but converted to oil firing. No. 452 was photographed at Oruro shed in 1956 on the Antofagasta (Chile) & Bolivia Railway.
[D. Ibbotson]

54

Kitson & Company 2-8+8-0T Kitson Meyer locomotive, one of three built in 1908 (Works Numbers 4580-2), for the 5 ft. 5$\frac{13}{16}$ in. gauge Great Southern Railway of Spain. [Renfe]

Kitson & Company 2-6-2+2-6-2 Kitson Meyer locomotive, one of two constructed in 1928, Works Numbers 5413/4, for the 2 ft. 6 in. gauge Kalka-Simla Railway in India. [Constable & Company]

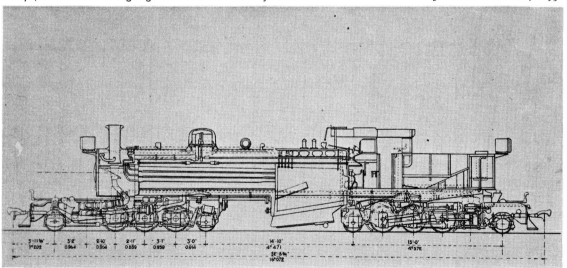

Kitson & Company 2-6+6-2T Kitson Meyer built in 1911; Works Number 4841. Supplied to the Antofagasta (Chile) & Bolivia Railway, this locomotive was withdrawn in 1929 at the time of the change of gauge in Bolivia from 2 ft. 6 in. to one metre. [Author's Collection]

Kitson & Company 0-8+6-0T combined rack and adhesion locomotive, Works Number 4669 of 1909. Supplied to the Argentine Transandine Railway, No. 41 was photographed at Mendoza in March 1972. [D. Ibbotson]

RACK-ADHESION MEYER LOCOMOTIVES

The metre gauge Transandine Railway was an important link in the railways connecting Argentina and Chile, opened throughout in 1910 when the summit tunnel, 10,512 ft. above sea level, was completed. The Chilian Transandine was a difficult line with 1 in 40 maximum adhesion grades, the upper section between Rio Blanco and the summit containing six Abt rack sections with grades of 1 in 12½/13.1/14.3, along with seven adhesion sections of about 1 in 40.

The Argentine Transandine was not as steep as the Chilian section containing 1 in 40 maximum adhesion grades to Punta de la Vacas from which point seven rack sections with 1 in 16⅔ grades carried the railway to the summit. Operation of a mountain railway is difficult enough with steep adhesion sections and even steeper rack sections interspersed, more particularly so when the whole is combined with 472 ft. radius curves on the adhesion sections and 590 ft. on the rack. Speeds were low due to the severe curvature and the impossibility of climbing such gradients fast, also there were real dangers involved in descending the rack too quickly. Another problem was the weather, for in the Andean winter between June and September severe snowfall could quickly cover any signs of a railway cutting or tunnel entrance.

At the time the line was opened 70 ton trains hauled by 40 ton locomotives working at about 5 m.p.h. on the rack sections were projected. Originally the Company operated 2-6-2 and 2-6-4 combined rack/adhesion tank locomotives built by Borsig of Berlin along with a 59 ton 4+4+4 Lima Shay which could haul 80 tons up the rack by adhesion only. Downhill, difficulty was experienced since the Shay could not safely manage 80 tons, although a repression brake was later fitted.

With the prospect of the International summit tunnel being completed, the consulting engineers had to obtain locomotives capable of hauling 120 ton trains on the rack at 6.2 m.p.h. uphill and 9.3 m.p.h. down. Eventually they produced plans for an 0-8+6-0 rack/adhesion locomotive utilising the Kitson Meyer form of articulation. The proposed locomotive had two steam bogies, the leading unit being an ordinary four-axle adhesion bogie driven from its own pair of cylinders and capable of hauling the locomotive up the 1 in 12½ rack grade. The rear three axle steam bogie had two cylinders and inside frames which served as outside frames for the two sets of rack pinions, this unit hauling the train. The Chilian Transandine was concerned about loss of adhesion should the leading bogie slip on the 1 in 12½ when the rails were iced up. To overcome this a third rack pinion was mounted between the first and second axles and an extra pair of small cylinders mounted on the adhesion bogie. The consulting engineers did not approve of these alterations but the prototype emerged from Kitsons works in Leeds in 1907 complete with these extra cylinders and third rack pinion. Later experience proved that the original plans would have produced a less complicated and more reliable locomotive and in 1911 the third rack pinion and extra cylinders were removed from all these locomotives. The Kitson Meyers were successful and hauled 140 tons on the rack.

The Company had considered other types of articulated but favoured the compact and easily maintained Kitson design. Another attraction was the relative ease of re-railing after snow clearance when the occasion demanded. The Mallet type was unsuitable because of restricted firebox size for the metre gauge and the Beyer Garratt was rejected as unsuitable for the rough work of snow clearing. The Chilian Transandine Railway did purchase two Esslingen modified rack/adhesion Mallet locomotives but these in no way came up to the Kitsons.

The Chilian section owned three Kitson Meyers and the Argentine Transandine had six. Five of the Argentine ones were noted at Mendoza in 1972, four dumped and one working. The sixth was said to be still working there but was not seen.

The Vulcan Ironworks of Wilkes-Barre in Pennsylvania introduced the Duplex in June 1931 with the completion of Works Number 4141, a 4 ft. 8½ in. gauge 0-4+4-0T based on the Meyer system. It had two independent steam bogies, each having a pair of cylinders mounted on the inner ends. A girder mainframe carried the wagon top boiler, cab, rear fuel and water compartments. This locomotives became No. 144 of the Dick Construction Company of Hazelton and was set to work at Audenried, Pennsylvania, about 25 miles south of Wilkes-Barre.

The Vulcan Ironworks introduced the Duplex simply because it had no articulated locomotive to offer and several of its customers had purchased Heisler articulateds. Vulcan had sold many locomotives to the coalfields of Pennsylvania and regarded this area as its own. When these customers turned to Heislers, Vulcan were annoyed and acquired a set of Heisler specifications, designing the Duplex to do all its opponent could do. With a rated tractive effort of 27,860 lbs., No. 4141 developed over 30,000 lbs. against a Dick Construction Heisler at Audenried on trial, and in terms of rated tractive effort per pound of weight, the Duplex was superior to its rivals. It had about one third more tractive effort than a 55-ton Heisler, nearly one sixth more than a 70-ton Shay and about one twentieth more than a 60-ton Climax.

In all, seven Duplex locomotives were constructed, the design having been introduced too late considering that Climax ceased construction in 1928, Willamette in 1929 and only about six Shay and thirty Heislers were built after 1930. The design was of course similar to the Kitson Meyer although the American technical press described it as "a development of the Davenport locomotive".

Vulcan Iron Works (of Wilkes-Barre, Pennsylvania) 0-4+4-0T Duplex, Works Number 4168 of 1934. When new this locomotive was delivered as No. 25 to the 4 ft. gauge Haddock Mining Company railway at Candlemas Colliery, in Pennsylvania, USA.

The boiler, frame and back head of a Vulcan Duplex which was to become 3 ft. 6 in. gauge Hill & Suender No. 11 (see below).

Vulcan Iron Works 0-4+4-0T Duplex; Works Number 4160 of 1932. This unit was employed in the coal stripping industry at Natalie in Northumberland County, Pennsylvania, as Hill & Suender No. 11.

DU BOUSQUET ARTICULATED LOCOMOTIVES

In the early 1900s the Chemin de fer du Nord of France required new motive power to replace the ageing four-cylinder compound 4-6-0s then hauling coal trains from the collieries of northern France. This traffic represented the principal freight on the Nord system and between Paris and Lens the 4-6-0s could handle 950 ton trains at 20 m.p.h. The section between Valenciennes and Hirson and also between Busigny and Hirson had opposing gradients of 1 in 83 and the trains had to be divided at Valenciennes or Busigny. To overcome this, the Chief Mechanical Engineer, Gaston du Bousquet, developed a large and powerful 0-6-2+2-6-0T articulated for the traffic.

The du Bousquet design employed two independent steam bogies and was a four-cylinder compound, the low pressure cylinders being on the leading unit, high pressure on the rear. The cylinders were mounted on the inner ends of each unit. A carrying axle was provided on each steam bogie to ease cylinder overhang. Bogie pivots were part of a continuous box section girder frame upon which the superstructure, comprising boiler, firebox, cab, water and fuel was mounted. The front bogie pin consisted of a spherical bearing of large diameter, the rear being a flat one. The boiler was also supported beneath the smokebox directly by the leading bogie frame whilst at the rear end of the firebox were circular bearing brackets attached to the rear bogie with extra supports under the cab doorways.

The first du Bousquet, No. 6121, was shown at the Liège Exposition in 1905 before being set to work on the coal traffic between the Nord and Est systems. Over the 1 in 83 sections where trains had previously been divided, the du Bousquet locomotives hauled 950 tons throughout at 12 m.p.h. On the easier graded section from Lens to Valenciennes these powerful locomotives ran their trains at 31-37 m.p.h.

48 were built for the Chemin de fer du Nord of France between 1905 and 1911. The Chemin de fer de l'Est of France had 13 identical locomotives and other du Bousquets operated on the Grand Ceinture Railway, this company owning 38. The Grand Ceinture handled most of the heavy transit freight traffic between various Paris area goods yards and these and the Est du Bousquets were used on this work, proving ideal since they could produce a high tractive effort and were highly flexible.

Outside France there were only two applications of the du Bousquet principle, the Société Anonyme des Forges Usines et Fonderies, of Haine St. Pierre, in Belgium, constructing a batch for the 4 ft. 8½ in. gauge Pekin-Hankow Railway in China, in 1906. These were built from the Nord drawings but varied in details. A further application was made in 1911 when the 5 ft. 6 in. gauge Andalusian Railway of Spain took delivery of a batch of similar machines from the Belgian makers, Usines Métallurgiques du Hainaut.

The French locomotives were held in high regard and the last one was withdrawn on the Grand Ceinture in 1952.

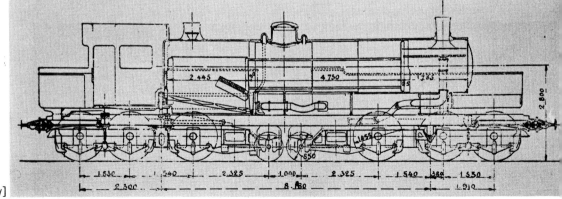

du Bousquet
0-6-2+2-6-0 for the
4 ft. 8½ in. gauge
Chemin de fer du
Nord, France.
[Constable & Company]

Nord du Bousquet at St. Pol in the summer of 1918, attached to the Railway Operating Department for banking duties.

[R. S. McNaught]

The Société Anonyme des Forges Usines et Fonderies, at Haine St. Pierre in Belgium, constructed some du Bousquet locomotives in 1906 for the 4 ft. 8½ in. gauge Pekin-Hankow Railway of China. These were similar to the Nord locomotives.

[Author's Collection]

SIX-ENGINE SENTINEL ARTICULATEDS

The Sentinel Waggon Works Ltd., of Shrewsbury, supplied several six-engined articulated locomotives to the metre gauge Colombian Railways of South America in 1934. The superstructure comprising Woolnough boiler, tanks, bunker and cab was mounted on a main frame carried on two six-wheel bogies, the outer axle of each unit being mounted in a Bissel-type truck. Each axle was separately driven through gearing by a small totally-enclosed steam engine mounted on the bogie. Each engine was a double acting compound, driving a crankshaft running in roller bearings and carrying at its centre a pinion which meshed with a gear wheel on the centre of the corresponding axle. The engines employed were standard Sentinel steam-waggon types and built in two stock sizes but fitted with different gear ratios. All the motion gear and crankshaft assembly was enclosed in a crank case partly filled with oil. Piston valves were actuated by Stephenson link motion. The working pressure of the Woolnough water tube boiler was 550 lbs. per square inch, live steam being reduced to about 140 lbs. before it was admitted to the low pressure cylinders.

The Sentinel Waggon Works claimed a 50 percent saving in fuel compared with conventional locomotives, one advantage being that steam could be raised from cold in less than half the normal time. One of these locomotives was sent to Belgium for trials on the line between Marche and Bastogne following agreement with the Société Nationale des Chemins de fer Vicinaux Belges, with satisfactory results.

Sentinel Wagon Works Ltd. (Shrewsbury) 0-6+6-0T six-engined gear-driven articulated built in 1934 for the Colombian Railways in South America.
[Author's Collection]

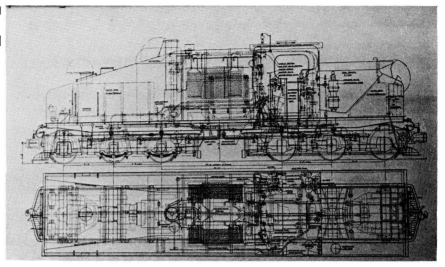

Diagram of the Sentinel
0-6+6-0T.
  [Author's Collection]

The Sentinel Wagon
Works 0-6+6-0T on
test on the Société
Nationale des Chemins
de fer Vicinaux Belges,
before shipment to
South America.
  [Author's Collection]

BEYER GARRATT ARTICULATEDS

In 1907 H. W. Garratt was employed as inspecting engineer for the New South Wales Government and in that capacity was a frequent visitor to the Gorton Works of Beyer Peacock. His original idea concerned mounting artillery on railway bogies and from this was developed the system of articulation which carries his name. Garratt applied for a patent in 1907, the basic idea consisting of a boiler and cab slung in a cradle frame between two steam bogies, these being pivot mounted to the boiler unit. Water and fuel supplies were mounted on the steam bogies, the overall arrangement permitting maximum size boilers and fireboxes, with large self-cleaning ashpans, limited only by the loading gauge of the railway concerned and the capabilities of the firemen employed. At first, Garratt was unable to find a locomotive builder sufficiently interested to finance and develop his idea and it appears to have been more by accident than by planning that Beyer Peacock decided to take it up. At that time they had received an enquiry from the Dundas Tramway in Tasmania, owners of a most unusual Hagans semi-articulated 2-6-4-0T. Possibly Beyer Peacock thought that since the Dundas Tramway owned a Hagans locomotive, they would not be interested in an unknown form of articulation—largely on the basis of once bitten, twice shy. At any event, Beyer Peacock, although not particularly interested in a one-off order for a new type of articulated, forwarded designs to Tasmania and in 1908 an order came back for two 0-4+4-0T compound Beyer Garratts with the cylinders mounted at the inner ends of the steam bogies. One of these two pioneer locomotives was purchased back by Beyer Peacock & Company in 1947, to be placed on display at their Gorton works, and this is now at the Boston Lodge works of the Festiniog Railway in Wales.

In 1911 a 2 ft. gauge Beyer Garratt was supplied to the Darjeeling-Himalaya Railway and this one was the prototype for future Garratt practice, having four simple expansion cylinders located at the outer ends of the steam bogies. These early Beyer Garratts were small narrow gauge locomotives and Beyer Peacock probably felt the type was limited to this market, fixing up a licensing arrangement with the Société Anonyme de Saint Léonard, of Liège, with the intention of entering the substantial market which then existed for small Mallets.

H. W. Garratt died in 1913, resulting in the further development of the Beyer Garratt being undertaken by Beyer Peacock & Company themselves and it was not until after the first world war that the impact of the type was really felt. It was sold to most countries but found its most successful market in Africa, particularly on the 3 ft. 6 in. gauge South African Railways. The type was produced in 2 ft., 2 ft. 6 in., 3 ft., one metre, 3 ft. 5½ in., 3 ft. 6 in., 4 ft. 8½ in., 5 ft., 5 ft. 3 in., and 5 ft. 6 in., gauges—with axle loadings ranging from 3¾ tons to 21 tons. Amongst the largest Beyer Garratt users were South African Railways who purchased approximately 440, Rhodesian Railways with 245 and the East African Railways who had about 155.

Unlike most articulateds, the Beyer Garratt was equally at home on express passenger workings and several different types were built solely for this purpose. The largest builder of Beyer Garratts was of course Beyer Peacock & Company Ltd. and many readers will be surprised to learn that the type has been built by various other firms including Sir W. G. Armstrong Whitworth & Company of Newcastle-on-Tyne, the North British Locomotive Company Ltd. of Glasgow, Hunslet Taylor & Company (Pty) Ltd, South Africa, John Cockerill of Seraing, Belgium, Forges et Acieries de Haine Saint Pierre of Belgium, and the Société Anonyme de Saint Léonard of Liège. In Germany the Beyer Garratt was constructed by the Hannoversche Maschienenfabrik (Hanomag) of Hanover, Henschel of Cassel, A. G. Krupp of Essen, Linke-Hoffman Werke, and J. A. Maffei of Munich. In France, the type was constructed by the Société Franco-Belge of Raismes. Other Garratt locomotives have been constructed by the Compania Euskalduna de Construccion y Reparacion de Buques of Bilbao in Spain, Babcock & Wilcox also of Bilbao, Ansaldo of Italy and by several Australian workshops including those of the West Australian Government Railways, builders of wartime Beyer Garratt locomotives.

Beyer Peacock & Company Ltd. 2-4+4-2T Beyer Garratt; one of three built in 1915, Works Numbers 5892-5894, for the 5 ft. 3in. gauge Sao Paulo Railway in Brazil. These were the first Beyer Garratts intended for use on express passenger trains.   [North West Museum of Science & Technology]

Beyer Peacock & Company Ltd 0-4+4-0T Beyer Garratt; one of two built in 1909, Works Numbers 5292 and 5293, for the 2 ft. gauge Tasmanian Government Railways' Dundas Tramway. These locomotives were compounds, with the cylinders on the inner ends of the bogies.   [North West Museum of Science & Technology]

Beyer Peacock & Company Ltd. 2-6-2+ 2-6-2 Beyer Garratt; one of three built in 1926, Works Numbers 6297-6299, for the 2 ft. 6 in. gauge Sierra Leone Government Railways. One of these locomotives was later converted to a 2-8-0+0-8-2T.
[North West Museum of Science & Technology]

Beyer Garratt in the sun at Freetown, Sierra Leone.
[D. Trevor Rowe]

Compania Minera de
Sierra Menera
Euskalduna-built
Garratt No. 502 and
North British
Locomotive Company
semi-articulated Mallet
No. 302 head a load of
empties back up to the
iron ore mines of Ojos
Negros in the Menera
mountains in Portugal,
1961.
    [D. Trevor Rowe]

Beyer Garratt No.
462.0404, built in 1931 by
the Compania
Euskalduna de
Construccion y
Reparacion de Buques
of Bilbao, heads a
Barcelona-Seville
express at Valencia
Termino station in 1961
on the 5 ft. 6 in. gauge
Renfe of Spain.
    [D. Trevor Rowe]

Euskalduna 2-6-2+ 2-6-2T Beyer Garratt No. 501 (Works Number 189 of 1930) banking a train near Puerto on the Portuguese mineral railway of the Compania Minera de Sierra Menera.

[D. Trevor Rowe]

Société St. Leonard of Liège 2-6+6-2T Beyer Garratt, Works Number 2036 of 1925, photographed in April 1961 at Sallent depot on the metre gauge Catalan Railway in Spain.

[D. Trevor Rowe]

No. 4025 of South
African Railways Class
GEA built by Beyer
Peacock & Company
Ltd. (4-8-2+2-8-4T
Beyer Garratt) heading
a train through the
Montague Pass in
October 1971.
      [D. Trevor Rowe]

3 ft. 6 in. gauge 4-8-2+
2-8-4T Beyer Garratt of
South African Railways
Class GMAM. Beyer
Peacock & Company
Ltd. built 33 of these in
1956-58 whilst others of
the same class were
constructed by the
North British
Locomotive Company
and Henschel & Son of
Cassel, Germany.
         [South African
              Railways]

Beyer Peacock-built 4-8-2+2-8-4T Beyer Garratt *Mount Meru*; Works Number 7634 of 1955, was locomotive number 5903 on the metre gauge East African Railways.   [North West Museum of Science & Technology]

Beyer Peacock & Company Ltd. 4-8-2+ 2-8-4T Beyer Garratt; Works Number 6531 of 1929. 3 ft. 6 in. gauge South African Railways locomotive number 2351 of Class GL. This photograph presents an interesting comparison with that above.
   [North West Museum of Science & Technology]

Another double Mountain type Beyer Garratt, this one belonging to the Sierra Leone Government Railways. No. 65 was built by Beyer Peacock & Company Ltd. in 1955 (Works Number 7709) and represented quite a machine for 2 ft. 6 in. gauge.   [North West Museum of Science & Technology]

South African Railways 3 ft. 6 in. gauge Beyer Garratt running at sea level on the Mossel Bay— Oudtshoorn section.
[Author's Collection]

The largest Beyer Garratt ever built emerged from the Gorton works of Beyer Peacock & Company Ltd., in 1932; a 4-8-2+2-8-4T ordered by Arcos Ltd. for Machtransimport of Leningrad, for the Soviet Railways. This $262\frac{1}{2}$ ton locomotive stood 17 ft. above rail level and was designed to haul 2,500 ton trains.

[North West Museum of Science & Technology]

Beyer Peacock & Company Ltd. 2-6-2+2-6-2T Beyer Garratt, locomotive number TC11 was one of seven built in 1958 for the Tsumeb Corporation. It was sold to the 2 ft. gauge South African Railways when the Corporation changed its gauge and it became SAR Class NG/G16.

[North West Museum of Science & Technology]

Beyer Peacock & Company designed and patented a development of the Beyer Garratt locomotive, 2-6-6-2+2-6-6-2, the outermost group at each end being integral with the main frame as in the Mallet. The boiler was carried between the engine units as in a conventional Garratt but each of these units was in effect a complete Mallet with two sets of six wheels, one fixed and one moveable. Each was driven by its own pair of cylinders, there being eight in all. The design was intended for South African Railways but no actual locomotive was constructed.

J. A. Maffei & Company of Munich altered the Beyer Garratt design in a number of ways, the first of these so-called Garratt-Union locomotives being constructed for South Africa in 1927. In this design the girder frame supporting the boiler was continued backwards, carrying also the water tank and coal bunker as in the Modified Fairlie type. Since there was no relative movement between the bunker and firebox it was possible to incorporate an automatic stoker of the Duplex type and this, of course, was the principal attraction of the Garratt-Union. Two classes entered service on the 3 ft. 6 in. gauge lines in South Africa, Class U being a 2-6-2+2-6-2 freight locomotive whilst Class GH was a heavy 4-6-2+2-6-4.

J. A. Maffei (Munich) 2-6-2+2-6-2 Union Garratt; Works Number 5673 of 1927, built under Beyer Peacock-Maffei patents for the 3 ft. 6 in. gauge South African Railways. Locomotive number 1370.

[Author's Collection]

SHAY ARTICULATED LOCOMOTIVES

In 1873 Ephraim Shay owned and operated a sawmill at Haring in Michigan, cutting bridge and building timbers. At that date business was bad, with two alternatives for Shay— either reduce expenses or close down. Various experiments were tried to reduce the cost of logging using horses, a tramway and a double truck flat car but this proved costly for the unbraked flat car gathered speed on the down grade and over-ran the horse, on one occasion killing it. Shay tried a small locomotive but the weight of this destroyed his track. However, he observed that the log cars weighing twice as much did no damage and he realised that the answer lay in transferring power to bogies instead of ordinary driving wheels, so avoiding damage to the track. During the winter, Shay rebuilt the little locomotive, conveying power as best he could to the bogies. Successive re-buildings by Shay and his mill blacksmith produced a crude but satisfactory locomotive which made logging more profitable. Another sawmill owner who was a friend of Shay found himself on the point of failure because of high expenses and asked if he would build him a similar loco-motive. Shay referred him to Carnes, Agerter & Company who supplied the machine during 1880. A second Shay was built later the same year for the 3 ft. gauge line of Cobbs &

Mitchell Lumber Company of Cadillac, in Michigan. Two 6 inch × 6 inch vertical cylinders drove a horizontal shaft which ran the full length of the locomotive on the right-hand side at wheel centre level. Shafts carried pinions and these meshed with bevel gears fastened to each bogie wheel, the latter being mounted in arch bar frames. The horizontal transmission shaft between the cylinders and bogies was provided with sliding sockets at the joints to permit easy running through curves. Universal joints were provided at the ends of each piece of the transmission shaft. A vertical boiler was centrally mounted with the water supply to the front and fuel to the rear.

Shay patented his design in June 1881 and shortly after disposed of the manufacturing rights to the Lima Machine Works of Lima, Ohio. Offset horizontal boilers soon replaced the vertical ones and Shay locomotives were built with two, three or four trucks. The type was popular throughout the American logging industry and was exported to other countries where severe grades were combined with sharp curvature. Approximately 2,770 were built in all and the design was so flexible that it was difficult to find two absolutely alike.

Carnes Agerter & Company of Lima, Ohio, 4+4 Shay. This was the second Lima Shay (Works Number 8 of 1880) for the 3 ft. gauge Cobbs & Mitchell Lumber Company in Michigan.   [Author's Collection]

An early Shay locomotive built at the Lima Machine Works in the 1880s. [R. Abbott]

WILLAMETTE GEARED LOCOMOTIVES

The Willamette Iron & Steel Works of Portland, in Oregon, entered the geared locomotive market when the Shay patents had become public property and they produced a locomotive almost identical to the Lima Shay. The first Willamette was supplied to the Coos Bay Lumber Company of Marshfield, Oregon, in November 1922 and had three powered bogies. In subsequent years the company constructed two two-truck and 31 three-truck articulateds.

Lima Machine Works 4+4+4 Shay with three cylinders for the English Lumber Company, USA. [R. Abbott]
Lima Machine Works 2 ft. gauge 4+4 Shay locomotive with three clyinders. Built for the H. H. Hall Construction Company, USA, in 1920. [R. Abbott]

CLIMAX ARTICULATED LOCOMOTIVES

The first Climax articulated was built in June 1891 by the Climax Manufacturing Company of Corry (Pennsylvania), for a 6 ft. gauge pole road, the Dallas & Ellendale. This locomotive had a vertical two-cylinder marine-type engine mounted on the centre line of the frame behind the back head. A transmission shaft ran along the centre of the locomotive, above the axles, driving each of these through a pair of bevel gears. This particular locomotive had a vertical boiler.

Later Climax locomotives had their cylinders mounted at an angle on both sides near the front of the boiler barrel, driving a cross shaft in front of the cab. This cross shaft was geared to a centre transmission shaft. Most had two powered bogies but in later years a number of three truck machines were constructed. They were widely used on American logging railroads, mountain lines and industrial railways where severe grades and sharp curves existed. A considerable number were exported to other parts of the world.

An early Class A Climax locomotive fitted with conventional railroad wheels. Alternative wheels were available allowing the Climax to run on pole roads or on tramroads laid with wooden track.
[Author's Collection]

Tee boiler Climax Number 5 at work in the New Zealand logging industry. Note the special wheels enabling the locomotive to run on wooden track.

[Alexander Turnbull Library, Wellington]

A later style Climax of Type B with a train
of logging trucks in a scenic setting in
New Zealand.
[Alexander Turnbull Library, Wellington]

◀

Class B Climax 4+4; Works Number 596
of 1905 was No. 4 on the 3 ft. gauge
Susquehanna & Eagles Mere Railroad
(a lumber road in north-east
Pennsylvania), photographed about 1910.
[R. Abbott]

SCHWARTZKOPFF CHAIN-DRIVE ARTICULATEDS

Designed and constructed by L. Schwartzkopff, of Berlin, this type of articulated employed a chain transmission. Each of the two steam bogies had a pair of cylinders mounted on the inner ends, driving a crank axle located between the driving axles which were coupled by chains. In service these chains were found to last between 9 and 12 months. The boiler, cab, rear water and fuel compartments were mounted on a main frame carried by the steam bogies. The first machine was supplied to Peru about 1925 and on a recent visit to South America the remains of a Schwartzkopff of this date were noted at Puerto Casado on the line owned by the Carlos Casado Company in Paraguay.

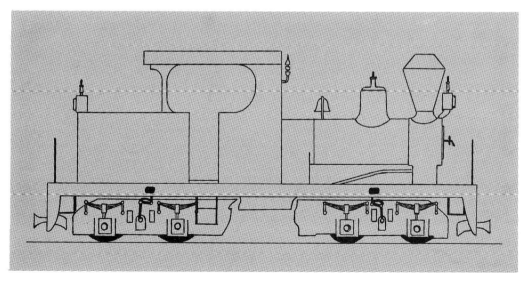

A drawing of the
Schwartzkopff chain-
driven locomotive.
[Author's Collection]

NEW ZEALAND 'BUSH' ARTICULATEDS

The New Zealand locomotive building firm of A. & G. Price Ltd., of Thames, were specialists in the manufacture of locomotives for use within the timber milling industry. Apart from 123 main line locomotives for New Zealand Railways, they produced 21 so-called 'bush' locomotives ranging from 0-4+4-0T to the 4+4+4+4 type of 1912-3. One of these came into the Railways Department stock when the Stores branch took over the Mountain Rimu Timber Company's operation at Mamaku. The locomotive illustrated on pages 82 and 83 was of Price Type 24 and could negotiate 99 ft. radius curves. It was powered by a two-cylinder vertical marine-type engine mounted at the rear of the cab. The design was basically an enlarged Climax Type A, drive being taken by lay shaft and a longitudinal drive shaft, through bevel gears to each axle. A 600 gallon water tank placed behind the cab was surmounted by a high bunker for the wood fuel. Equipment included steam brakes working on all wheels. The Railways Department sold this locomotive in 1928 and its subsequent history is not known. It had 2 ft. diameter driving wheels, 140 lb. boiler pressure, $7\frac{1}{2}$ in. × 10 in. cylinders and weighed approximately 20 tons.

A. & G. Price Bros. bush locomotive used at the New Zealand Railways
State sawmill at Mamaku in 1916.

[Alexander Turnbull Library, Wellington]

A. & G. Price Bros. (of Thames, New Zealand) articulated locomotive with a
load of logs in New Zealand.   [Alexander Turnbull Library, Wellington]

An interesting scene with a timber tram hauling a load of logs over timber trestling at Raurimu in New Zealand. This locomotive was built by A. & G. Price Bros.
[Alexander Turnbull Library, Wellington]

A. & G. Price Bros. Type D articulated locomotive: Knight's timber tram at Raurimu, New Zealand. [Alexander Turnbull Library, Wellington]

NORTH BRITISH MODIFIED FAIRLIES

The so-called Modified Fairlie design was produced by the North British Locomotive Company of Glasgow, as a competitor for the Beyer Garratt market in South Africa. The Modified Fairlie had little in common with the true Fairlie design other than the inclusion of two steam bogies and although it looked like a Beyer Garratt was actually a modified Kitson Meyer. The bar framed steam bogies were extended outwards as in the Beyer Garratt and the superstructure (comprising front water tank, boiler, cab and rear fuel and water compartments), were mounted on a continuous girder frame as in the Kitson Meyer design. Pivots were located at the centres of the rigid wheelbases. A socket was attached to the underside of the boiler barrel and in this worked a pivot attached to the leading steam bogie. The back end of the firebox rested on both sides of the rear steam bogie frames by spherical seated bearings and sliding plates carried by brackets attached to the frames.

The prototype was constructed for the South African Railways in 1924 (SAR Class FC) and this was followed in 1926 by four similar 2-6-2+2-6-2 locomotives (SAR Class FD). The solitary Class FC remained in service until 1939 and the Class FD were withdrawn between 1957-9. Henschel supplied eleven similar but larger 2-8-2+2-8-2 in 1927-28 (SAR Class HF), and these lasted until 1950-51.

The type was not further constructed since the Beyer Garratt was found to be a far more successful machine. The Modified Fairlie ran into problems because of the excessive overhang and water splashing about in the leading tank. This put stress on the pivots which then ceased working correctly, resulting in the unit having to be taken out of service for repairs which subsequently proved expensive.

North British Locomotive Company 2-6-2+2-6-2T modified Fairlie, locomotive number 2310 built 1924; South African Railways 3 ft. 6 in. gauge, Class FC.
[South African Railways]

86

Interior of the North British Locomotive Company works at Glasgow showing several
Modified Fairlies under construction for the 3 ft. 6 in. gauge South African Railways.
[Mitchell Library]

North British
Locomotive Company
2-6-2+2-6-2T modified
Fairlie No. 2323 of the
3 ft. 6 in. gauge South
African Railways.
[Mitchell Library]

Another works
photograph depicting
the North British
modified Fairlie
locomotive.
[Mitchell Library]

BALDWIN GEARED ARTICULATEDS

The Baldwin Locomotive Works produced five articulated tank locomotives in competition with the Climax, after which the first four were patterned. Inclined cylinders were located in a position similar to those of the larger Climax, driving a countershaft placed transversely beneath the boiler. This countershaft was bevel geared to two longitudinal shafts, one of which drove the front bogie, the other the rear. When a third truck was employed, power was carried to it by a third longitudinal shaft. The first of these geared locomotives was a two-truck model which shunted the Baldwin Locomotive Company's Eddystone Works.

Two three-truck locomotives followed and the fourth, a two-trucker, was sold to the metre gauge Leopoldina Railway of Brazil, in 1914.

The final locomotive was built in 1915 and was of a completely new design. It had three cylinders horizontally placed beneath the boiler, driving a line shaft along the right hand side of the frame, which by bevel gears and jack shafts transmitted power across to the bogies driving the geared wheels on the left side. None of these designs was particularly successful in attracting orders and Baldwin produced no further geared articulated locomotives.

Baldwin Locomotive Works geared articulated locomotive for the Marysville & Northern Railroad of Sedro Wooley, Washington, USA.

Baldwin Locomotive Works geared articulated locomotive, patterned after the larger Type B Climax. This is No. 106 on the metre gauge Leopoldina Railway in Brazil.

The Baldwin Locomotive Works final true articulated, intended for use within the logging industry, was built in 1915 but was not a success.

HEISLER ARTICULATED LOCOMOTIVES

Constructed by the Stearns Manufacturing Company of Erie, Pennsylvania, the first Heisler was shipped to Mexico on 20 August 1894. Like the Shay and the Climax, the Heisler was mainly employed over roughly-laid logging railways in the United States but it was used also on mountain lines and other localities where steep gradients and sharp curves abounded. Most Heisler locomotives were two truckers but Stearns introduced a "New Class 90 West Coast Special" three-truck model which was regarded as their answer to Lima's Pacific Coast Shay.

In the Heisler locomotive, transmission was by means of gears and side rods, the wheels of each bogie being connected by side rods. The cylinders were mounted on the main frame and set at 90 degrees to each other, both driving a single throw crank shaft, power being transmitted through a central shaft which ran the whole length of the locomotive at a point above the bogie axles. Drive was taken to the outermost axle of each truck and power was transmitted to this axle through bevel gears. The other axle in each truck received its drive by means of side rods.

Stearns Manufacturing Company of Erie, Pennsylvania, 0-4+4-0T Heisler articulated.
[Author's Collection]

AVONSIDE GEARED LOCOMOTIVES

In 1930 the Avonside Engine Company of Bristol constructed an articulated diesel locomotive for work on the Ellingham Estate plantation railway in South Africa and this proved to be highly satisfactory.

In 1931 when orders were received from other South African plantations, the same system of articulation was decided on, but as a comparison the new locomotives were to be steam driven, with a totally enclosed engine and gear drive.

Two different locomotives were designed, the smaller a two-cylinder 0-4+4-0T for use on poorly laid track comprising 18 lbs./yd. rail and with curves of exceptionally small radius. A right-angled "Vee" type engine and totally enclosed modified Hackworth valve gear were provided, the cylinders being mounted at an angle to the boiler. The engine unit drove totally enclosed worm gear units mounted on the outer axles of each bogie by universally jointed cardan shafts, the bogie axles being coupled by side rods. On test at the builders the locomotive performed well, running over irregular track easily and traversing curves down to 50 ft. radius.

The larger and more powerful locomotive was required to haul 100 tons on 1 in 35 at 8 m.p.h. minimum over the main lines of the plantation railways which were laid with 30 lbs./yd. rail. This machine had four cylinders, the adjacent ones at each side driving on to opposed cranks. Equipment included an eight element superheater, steam sanding plus steam and hand brakes. It developed a tractive effort of 11,811 lbs. at 80 per cent boiler pressure and weighed 23 tons in working order.

The Avonside Company built one four-cylinder locomotive for Natal Estates and three two-cylinder locomotives; one each for Illoya, Renishaw and Sezela estates. All were 2 ft. gauge. The design was not further produced by the company, but when they closed down, the Hunslet Engine Company of Leeds built one two-cylinder and two four-cylinder locomotives for use on plantation railways in Natal. The Hunslet design differed from that of Avonside in using bevel gears instead of a worm drive. The design was not further produced, the various sugar plantations turning to diesel power after the war.

Avonside Engine Company Ltd. articulated 4+4 diesel plantation locomotive built in 1930 for the 2 ft. gauge Ellingham Estate railway in South Africa.

[Author's Collection]

93

Two different types of articulated steam locomotives were constructed by the Avonside Engine Company Ltd., of Bristol, for plantation service. This photograph is of the smaller two-cylinder version; Works Number 2057 of 1931, delivered to the 2 ft. gauge railway owned by Renishaw Estates.   [Hunslet Engine Company]

One of the larger four-cylinder versions intended for mainline work on sugar estate lines built by the Avonside Engine Company; Works Number 2059 of 1931, delivered to Natal Estates. [Hunslet Engine Company]

A 15" GAUGE ARTICULATED

In 1928 the 15 in. gauge Ravenglass & Eskdale Railway Company created the *River Mite* from a 4-6-2 locomotive, the resulting 4-6-0+0-6-4 being constructed in the Company's shops at Ravenglass, Cumberland.

In the reconstructed locomotive, the main frames were removed in front of the firebox and steel side frames connecting front and rear steam bogies were bolted on both sides of the central pivot castings. These frames extended above the coupled wheels of both steam bogies, dropping downwards in the centre beneath the deep Belpaire firebox and cab. The pivot castings were fixed beneath the new,

large boiler and under the tender section which had to be raised to allow clearance for the rear driving wheels. Steam pipes to both units were fitted with "Flextel" joints and exhaust pipes were of phosphor bronze flexible metallic tubing. Exhaust from the cylinders of the leading unit was turned into the chimney in the usual way whilst that from the rear engine passed through a Weir feed water heater located at the extreme rear of the tender, from which point the feed water was delivered to the boiler by a Weir feed pump.

On test this locomotive was found to be steady running and a speed of 38 m.p.h. was reached.

The reconstructed Ravenglass & Eskdale locomotive *River Mite* in April 1928, in its original rebuilt form. Sir Aubrey Brocklebank saw it and told them in no uncertain terms to lower the cab!

[D. Ferreira, Ravenglass & Eskdale Railway Co. Ltd.]